Letterland

16 pages

Early Years Workbook 1

Letters: a-f

Name:

Aa

Look for Annie Apple's letters in the apple tree. Make them red.

Write Annie Apple's letter here.

Only one picture in each row begins with Annie Apple's sound. Draw a circle around it.

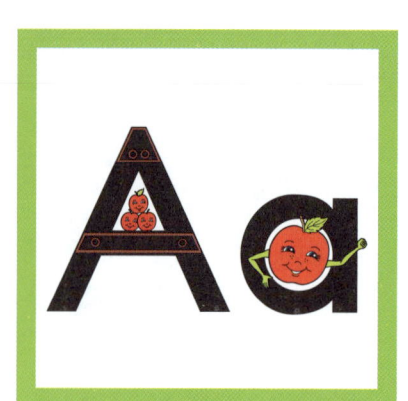

Colour the spaces with Annie Apple's letter in them. The animal begins with Annie's sound. What is it?

I have coloured an alligator.

Sometimes Mr A, the Apron Man, says his name in words. Join Mr A to the things that begin with his sound.

Colour the balloons with Bouncy Ben's letters on them. Then join them to Bouncy Ben.

Write Bouncy Ben's letter here.

Find the things that begin with Bouncy Ben's sound. Make them blue.

Bouncy Ben's box

Can you draw something to eat that begins with my sound?

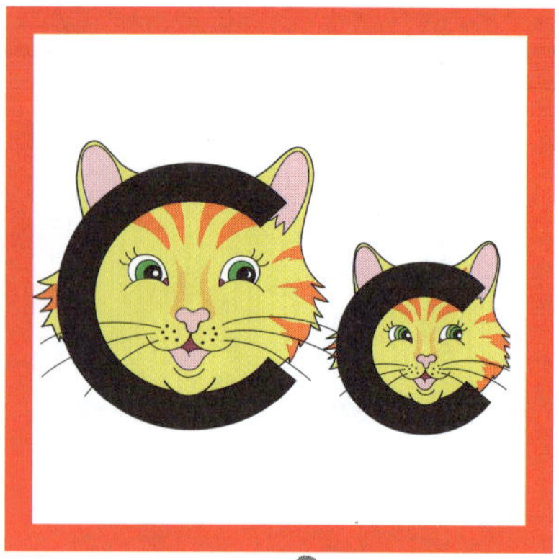

Find Clever Cat's letters in the Letterland castle. Make them red.

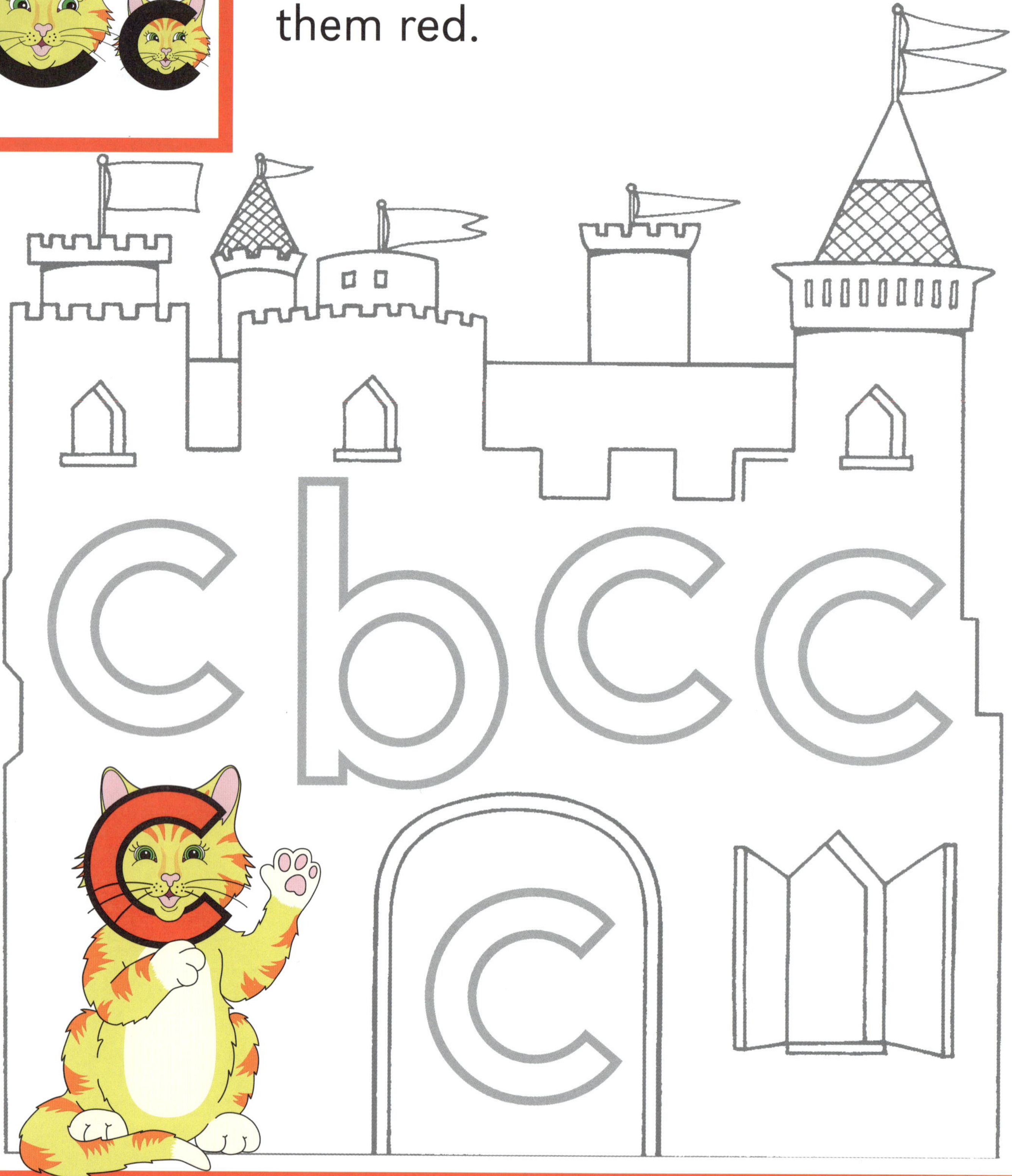

Write Clever Cat's letter here.

c c

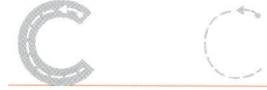

Only one picture in each row begins with Clever Cat's sound. Draw a circle around it.

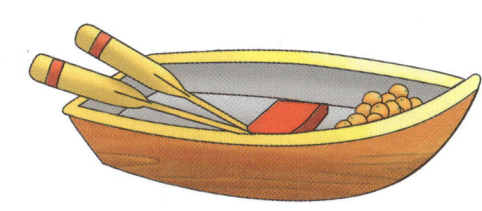

Help Dippy Duck find her letters on the drum. Make them orange.

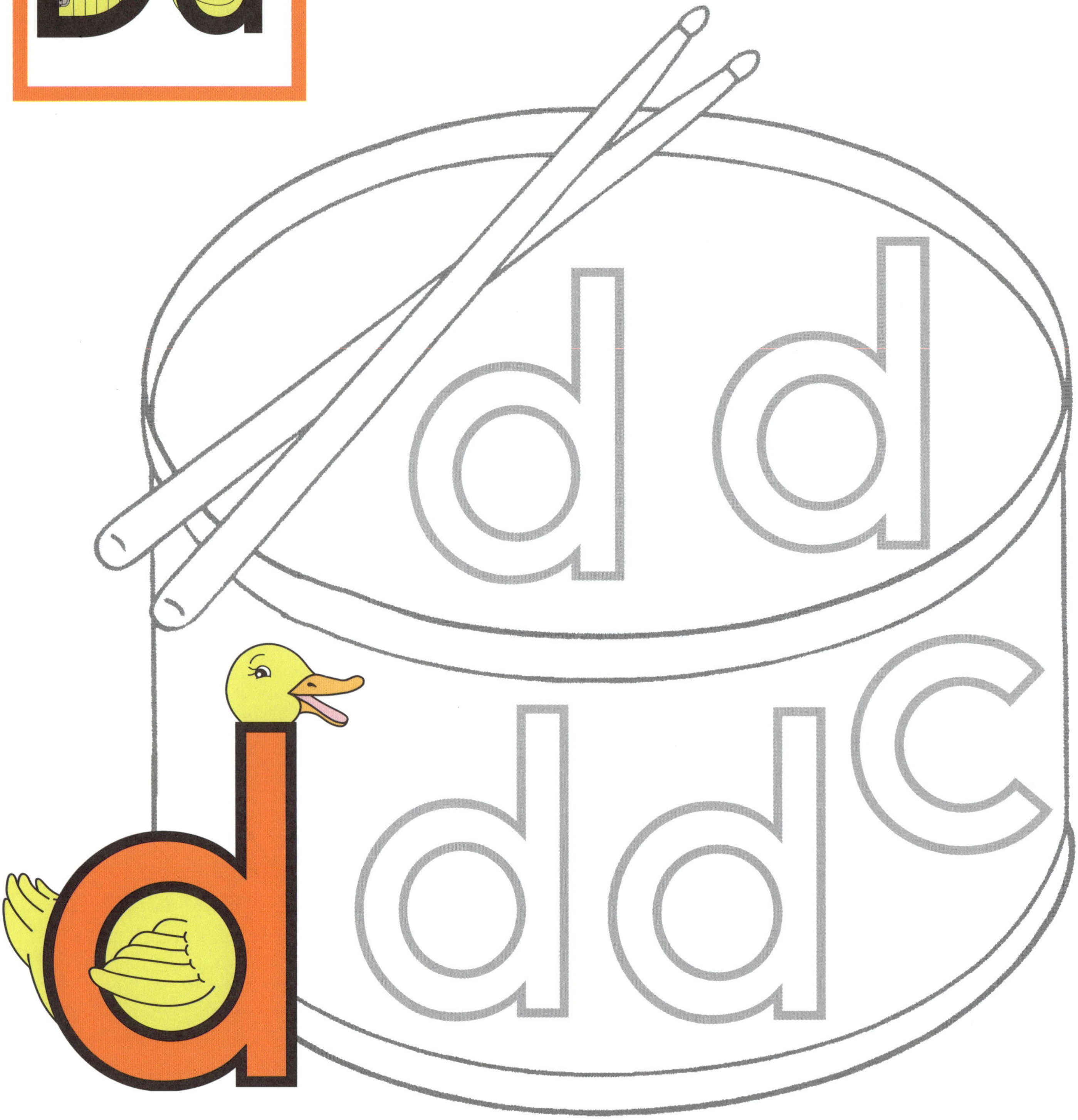

Write Dippy Duck's letter here.

Draw a line to join each animal to its shadow. Cross out the animal that does not begin with Dippy Duck's sound.

Draw something I might like for dinner.

Find the eggs with Eddy Elephant's letters on them. Make them red.

Write Eddy Elephant's letter here.

Circle the things that begin with Eddy Elephant's sound.

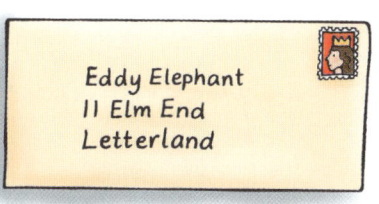
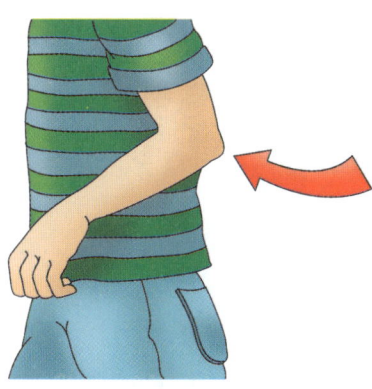
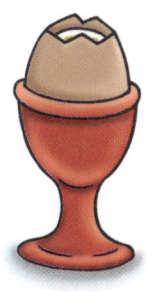

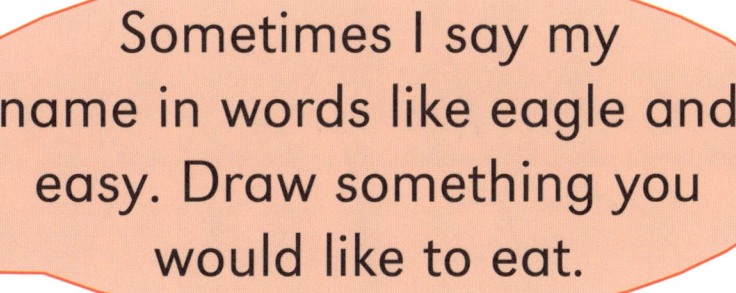

Sometimes I say my name in words like eagle and easy. Draw something you would like to eat.

Find four of Firefighter Fred's letters in the flames of the fire. Make them red and yellow.

Write Firefighter Fred's letter here.

14

Join the dots to find something that begins with Firefighter Fred's sound.

Draw something that begins with my sound.

Look at the names under each picture.
Then draw the Letterlander.

Annie Apple	Bouncy Ben	Clever Cat
Dippy Duck	Eddy Elephant	Firefighter Fred

Published by Letterland International Ltd. 8/10 South Street, Epsom, Surrey, KT18 7PF, UK
© Letterland International 2006
ISBN: 978-1-86209-349-2

First published 1997.
This revised edition published 2006.
Reprinted 2008, 2011, 2012, 2014, 2018, 2020, 2021, 2023.
18 17 16 15 14

LETTERLAND™ is a trademark of Letterland International Ltd.

Written by Louis Fidge
Illustrated by Anna Jupp and Kathy Baxendale

Code: T59
ISBN 978-1-86209-349-2

Consultant: Lyn Wendon, originator of Letterland
All rights reserved. No part of this publication may be reproduced, stored in a retrieval system, or transmitted in any form or by any means, electronic, mechanical, photocopying, recording or otherwise, without the prior permission of the Publisher or a licence permitting restricted copying in the United Kingdom issued by the Copyright Licensing Agency Ltd, 90 Tottenham Court Road, London W1P 0LP.

British Library Cataloguing in Publication Data. A catalogue record for this book is available from the British Library.

Printed in Guangdong Province, China.

See our full range at: www.letterland.com